THE LIFE AND TIMES
OF
SADAKICHI HARTMANN

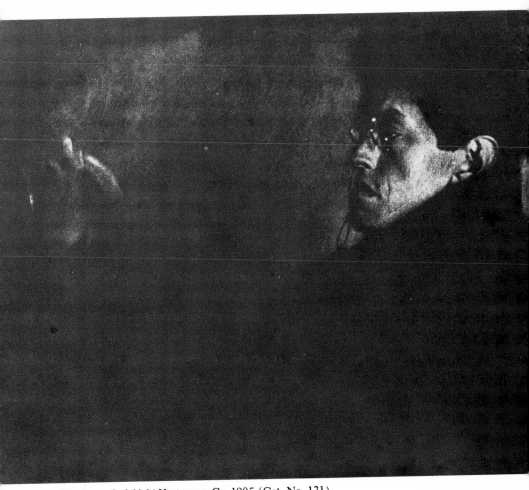

Steichen: *Sadakichi Hartmann, Ca.* 1905 (Cat. No. 121)

THE LIFE AND TIMES OF SADAKICHI HARTMANN
1867-1944

*If one hadn't been oneself, it wd. have
been worthwhile being Sadakichi.*
                    —*Ezra Pound*

AN EXHIBITION
Presented and Co-sponsored by the University Library
and
The Riverside Press-Enterprise Co.
at the
University of California, Riverside
May 1 to May 31, 1970

Published and Printed
by
Rubidoux Printing Co.
Riverside, California

Introduction

A grotesque etched in flesh by the drunken Goya of Heaven. A grinning, obscene gargoyle on the Temple of American Letters. Superman-bum. Half God, half Hooligan; all artist. Anarch, sadist, satyr. A fusion of Jap and German, the ghastly experiment of an Occidental on the person of an Oriental. Sublime, ridiculous, impossible. A genius of the ateliers, picture studios, ginmills, and East Side lobscouse restaurants. A dancing dervish, with graceful, Gargantuan feet and a mouth like the Cloaca Maxima. A painter out of Hakusai, Manet, Whistler. Result: fantastic realism. A colossal ironist, a suave pessimist, a Dionysiac wobbly.

Thus critic Benjamin De Casseres described Sadakichi Hartman in 1926 in Mencken's *American Mercury,* terming him as born out of his age," . . . a man who belonged in Cellini's gang or with the rowdy geniuses of the Mermaid Tavern." Indeed, as early as 1915, the Greenwich Village publicist Guido Bruno, while hailing Sadakichi as the unchallenged King of Greenwich Village, still spoke of him as a bad actor who should have died a decade earlier "instead of insisting upon living and being a monument of his own."

Through the remainder of his long life, Hartmann, who had bridged the period between Walt Whitman and the French Symbolists to the Jazz Age Bohemians who flocked to Greenwich Village from 1917 to 1923, seemed increasingly an anachronism to many, the last Bohemian hurling his defiance at "stagnant crowd-thinking and mass-meeting mentality" in works no one would publish. At last, with most of his early writings forgotten, he appeared to be no more than a seedy iconoclastic vagabond from the Mauve Decade, the man Gene Fowler fondly called "the magnificent charlatan." Only a few critics and writers such as Holger Cahill sensed the essential timelessness of Hartmann, his ability to make his way unerringly in every era to those things that have eternal value.

Today this man in the Prince Albert jacket, who surveys the world confidently from a pedestal in J. C. Strauss' 1896 photograph, appears surprisingly contemporary. He edited and published two of the first *avant-garde* art magazines in America. When many American artists and writers were fleeing to Paris as expatriates to join the Symbolists, Hartmann carried the Symbolist movement to this country and became its champion. In 1897, he drafted a script for the first psychedelic light show, noting that its presentation would have to await the invention of chemical, mechanical, or electrical means for projection. In 1902, he held the first perfume concert in New York City.

Long before the Imagists, at least as early as 1906, Hartmann was experimenting with *Haiku* and *Tanka* verse forms. He was instrumental in getting American photographers out of their studios and onto the streets of America, challenging them to innovate and develop their media. When James Gibbons Huneker charged that the Young American Painters Show of 1910 was a "revolution that doesn't revolve," it was Hartmann who understood that the turn to color was the war cry of the future, countering, "And time will show it is the most candid, the sanest, and most logical, if not the only way, of solving the vital problems of American art." And again, anticipating the future, it was Hartmann in 1923 who urged composers to experiment with "electro-magnetic music whose vibrations do not simulate orchestral instruments, but open up horizon-less vistas of virgin sound."

Open throughout May in the new Gallery of the University of California Library, Riverside, the Sadakichi Hartmann exhibition attempts to bring some belated recognition to one of the most neglected figures in American art and letters. The exhibit, titled *The Life and Times of Sadakichi Hartmann*, reflects creative work in many areas in which Hartmann was both a stimulus and a catalyst of literary and artistic activity.

Son of a multi-lingual and affluent German trader and a Japanese mother, Carl Sadakichi Hartmann was born in about 1867 on the island of Desima in Nagasaki harbor. After his mother, Osada, died in childbirth, Sadakichi and an elder brother, Taru, were taken to Hamburg, Germany, where they were brought up in luxury and given excellent schooling, primarily under the care of a wealthy uncle and their grandmother. Sadakichi was baptized a Lutheran, attended private schools (reading all of the works of Goethe and Schiller by the age of nine), and wore a uniform for a time at a preparatory naval school at Steinwaerder, Hamburg. Upon the remarriage of his father, Hartmann was placed in a naval academy in Kiel, but he rebelled against the Teutonic discipline and ran away to Paris. His angered father disinherited him, shipping the thirteen or fourteen-year-old boy off to an uncle in America.

When he arrived on a hot June day in 1882 in America, Hartmann discovered an environment that was, by comparison with his aristocratic surroundings in Germany, drab and barren. Working at menial jobs in printing and engraving shops, he discovered the Philadelphia Mercantile Library and spent his nights studying a variety of subjects, steadily gravitating toward the arts in search of a career. He visited Walt Whitman at Camden, and occasionally translated German correspondence for the aged and ailing poet. These visits are recorded by Hartmann in a small book entitled *Conversations with Walt Whitman* (1895).

During intermittent associations with the poet, Hartmann made four summer trips to Europe to further his study of literature, the theatre, and the visual arts. He studied stage machinery under Lautenschlaeger at the Royal Theatres, Munich, and art and literature in Berlin, Brussels, and Paris. He met Liszt, Bjornson, Carducci, and Gabriel Max, glimpsed Ibsen in awe from a distance, and was briefly a protege of Paul Heyse. During a trip through

Belgium and Holland in 1888, he spent three months of near-starvation in London, where he also met Swinburne and the Rossettis. In 1891, he journeyed to Europe as a foreign correspondent for the McClure Syndicate, interviewing many of the most prominent artists, writers, and poets of the day. He became acquainted with Stephane Mallarmé in Paris, and continued corresponding with the poet as late as 1897. In one of his articles ("A Tuesday Evening with Stephane Mallarmé"), he described the literary salon of the Symbolist poet. His subsequent studies of the Symbolist movement are reflected not only in much of the art criticism and many of the essays he wrote in the 1890's, but in his own plays and poetry.

As an art critic, Hartmann began writing essays for the Philadelphia newspapers in the 1880's. Between 1887 and 1889, he essayed the role of a Society Lion in Boston, giving readings, receptions, and concerts. Here he also wrote for the *Advertiser* and the *Transcript*, as well as for *Poet-Lore*, *The Theatre*, and *The People*. In literary circles, he met Lowell, Whittier, Holmes, and John Boyle O'Reilly. An effort to introduce Ibsen to America failed through lack of sufficient financial backing. Disillusioned, Hartmann spent several nomadic years in New York, barnstorming, engaging in hack writing, frequenting the Cafe Manhattan, and finally becoming discouraged to the point of attempting suicide.

While serving on the staff of the *Weekly Review* (1893), Hartmann issued 1,000 copies of his symbolist drama *Christ,* deemed by James Gibbons Huneker as "absolutely the most daring of all decadent productions." Almost all copies of the play were burned in Boston by the New England Watch and Ward Society, and Hartmann was arrested and spent Christmas week in Charles Street Jail, No. 2. This play was followed by his second symbolist drama *Buddha* (1897), which Vance Thompson referred to as "strange, gaudy, fantastic — a thing all color and incense; something gilded and monstrous and uncouth as the temple of Benares." Other religious dramas also followed: *Confucius, Mohammed, Moses,* and the unpublished *Baker Eddy.* A volume of short stories, *Schopenhauer in the Air,* appeared in 1899.

In 1893, Hartman launched his magazine the *Art Critic,* visiting over 750 studios in Boston, New York, and Philadelphia to drum up subscriptions. In an 1894 letter which addresses Hartmann as "My Dear Symbolist," the noted American muralist F. D. Marsh writes from Paris to describe meetings with Whistler and Sargent and his own enthusiasm in acting as an unofficial promoter of Hartmann abroad. But the magazine was soon doomed to failure; Hartmann had ranged too far ahead in his appreciation of European dramatists and painters, and America was incredibly indifferent and unreceptive to what had already been accepted on the Continent.

Hartmann was forced once more to turn his hand to what he considered hack work and journalism. Between 1898 and 1902, he turned out more than 350 sketches on New York life — ranging from studies of the poor to essays on high society — for the *New York Staats-Zeitung.* He served on the staff of *The Criterion,* wrote numerous articles on pictorial photography, and lectured widely on art. He also continued his efforts as a dramatist, and his realist play, *A Tragedy in a New York Flat*, was praised by Edmund Clarence Stedman in 1896. He recognized early that he lacked the talent to achieve fame as an artist, but throughout his life he painted and did pastels (almost 350 works in this medium), and his first exhibition of pastels was held in 1894. His pastels were often strikingly interesting, enough so that he was exhibited with Glackens, Fuhr, Perrine, and Lawrence at the Allen Gallery in 1900. He was also a critic of the dance and had unique ability as a dancer. Edward Weston said that no woman could approach "his feeling and understanding" for this art form.

In 1896, the same year that Alfred Stieglitz launched his *Camera Notes*, Hartmann attempted to revive his art magazine under the name of *Art News* in New York City. The venture soon failed, although artists such as Augustus St. Gaudens hailed Hartmann for his perspicuity in art matters. Stieglitz was quick to recognize that Hartmann was a man he needed. During the next two decades, Hartmann was at his most prolific, contributing important critiques on both art and photography to Stieglitz's *Camera Notes* and later to his more famous and innovative *Camera Work*.

Hartmann's first book on art, *Shakespeare in Art*, was published in 1900. His two-volume *History of American Art*, used as a standard text-book for many years and revised in 1938, was published in 1901. Other works of a popular nature on art followed, including *Japanese Art* (1903) and *The Whistler Book* (1910). Some of these works appear to have been hastily turned out by a man whose reputation as an art critic was rapidly growing. Meanwhile, his most incisive essays were being published by Stieglitz, with whom he enjoyed a respectful relationship, and in the pages of many now defunct journals. Many of his pioneering essays on photography as an art form and photographic techniques were published under the pen-name of Sidney Allan.

Among photographers whom Hartmann wrote about with originality, tact, and discrimination were Steichen, Keiley, White, Stieglitz, Eugene, Käsebier, Curtis, Strand, and Day. He also encouraged recognition of many contemporary painters and sculptors, e.g., Ryder, Tryon, Maurer, Hartley, Marin, Sloan, Luks, Lawson, Henri, and Max Weber. Similarly, in a later period, he promoted the work of Bellows, Thomas Hart Benton, Grant Wood, and others whose reputations testify to his prescience. In a recent letter, prior to this exhibition, Thomas Hart Benton wrote to say Hartmann "was far more intelligent about art problems than Huneker, and that a collection of his writings, letters, and other kinds, is due." His exotic Eurasian face made him a favorite subject of painters, sculptors, and photographers. He was painted by many of the great and near great, and, as he once said, "photographed by everybody."

The many-sided Hartmann has left diverse impressions; he could be enigmatic as well as uncompromisingly clear in his positions: "I am neither a freethinker who denies everything in playful irony, nor a devotee capable of performing rituals with a constant, bewildered enthusiasm. My ways are those of an agnostic. My father was a genuine freethinker; the rest of my family were mildly Lutheran. My stepmother was a Catholic. One of my aunts a French Jewess. My mother presumably was a Buddhist. These influences shaped my early view point." Near the end of his life, living in poverty on the Morongo Indian Reservation in Banning, California, he could say in summary: "I have devoted my long literary career largely to a promotion of a National U.S. Art and a lifelong plea for tolerance in religious matters. I wrote six dramas to prove that every religion has profound merits and deplorable defect. . . ."

Hartmann's entire life seems to have been an impassioned search for identity. *En route* he assumed many roles and guises: the sensitive, austere young poet and dramatist of the 1890's; the iconoclastic, fiercely uncompromising art lecturer of the turn of the century; the serious Sidney Allan with the omnipresent cigar and eye-piece; the roistering irresponsible King of Greenwich Village; and finally the aged clown in rags, court jester to the John Barrymore circle in Hollywood.

Although he was far less political than aesthetic in orientation ("I was always somewhat of an esthetic sybarite, looking primarily for manifestations of Plato's fine frenzy, Aristotle's purification of thought and sentiment, and Schopenhauer's moments of cognition."), Hartmann was a participant in the anarchist movement, joining Emma Goldman, Edwin Bjorkman, and John R. Coryell in founding the magazine *Mother Earth.* While he remained friendly with the anarchists, he never was able to commit himself to the movement in a genuinely activist way. Rather, he remained throughout his life skeptical, even pessimistic, about extreme political ideologies. As for the possibility that anarchism might work, his philosopher Kung in *Confucius* (1923) warns: "A cook is needed even for the most frugal brew."

From the turn of the century to the end of his life, he lectured on art and photography in cities throughout the nation. He assisted in bringing together various collections, reorganized art departments in libraries and museums, and stimulated interest in art in many cities from New York to Los Angeles. He was instrumental in discovering many young artists, whom he spoke of as "my art children," young men and women who in turn responded to the elderly Hartmann with fierce, devoted partisanship.

Throughout his life, Hartmann suffered from severe asthmatic attacks which became worse as the years went by, making it impossible for him to work at any steady job, and forcing him by the early 1920's to settle in the San Gorgonio Pass near Beaumont. He continued to make lecture forays eastward, but his health steadily deteriorated, and more and more he relied heavily on alcohol. During these years of physical and professional decline, his increased drinking, the shambles he made of his private life, his dependence upon patronage which he exacted from friends and admirers as tribute, and his acting out of Bohemian roles made him appear to many to be a grotesque caricature of the artist *manque*— even a charlatan.

He cultivated Hollywood, trying to write motion picture scripts. He wrote the first script for *Don Quixote,* but it was never filmed. For many years he was Hollywood columnist for *The Curtain*, published in England. He even appeared in a brief part as the Court Magician in Douglas Fairbanks' *The Thief of Bagdad*. As the years passed, he did less and less publishing on art, although between 1923 and 1932 he struggled intermittently on a 278,000-word book, *Esthetic Verities,* a critical summing-up of all his ideas on art. Occasionally, in the pages of *Art Digest* and other magazines, there appeared Hartmann's annual Art Handicap Derby in which he placed his bets on future winners. His best works had passed silently into oblivion. By the 1920's, noted artists who had once been his friends looked upon him as the disreputable Gully Jimson of American art. Even Jo Davidson, who had rousted with him in New York and written him enthusiastically from Paris in the early 1900's, wrote of Hartmann in his biography as a more casual acquaintance than appears to be indicated by recent evidence. There were a few last sparks, among them an impressive book titled *The Last Thirty Days of Christ,* praised by Ezra Pound and eulogized by Benjamin De Casseres as one of the strikingly original works of American literature.

Although a failure in Hollywood, Hartmann found himself adopted as a drinking companion by the John Barrymore crowd, a group that often centered its doings in the studio of artist John Decker on Bundy Drive. Before this group, Sadakichi displayed his mordant wit and fatalistic humor. His tales of Whitman and Mallarme, of Isadora Duncan and Greenwich Village characters — tales related with a half-mocking quality and often fantastic embellishments — were regarded as sheer invention by the Hollywood crowd that kept the old man in drinks in order to be entertained by his talk, recitations, and bizarre dancing. They liked this shabby self-proclaimed genius with termagantish tongue, and they brought him to parties as a put-on guest to shock the easily outraged. But they were convinced, nonetheless, that he was essentially a hoax and a poseur. How else explain the sly mockery of a man who would outrage all credibility by beginning an anecdote: "On a day like this, there were Rodin, Whitman, myself and three beers in a cafe in Vienna . . ."

One should know, however, that during this same period Hartmann was also well known to a very different circle, whose activities centered around the home of a vivacious young woman, Margery Winter, at 1640 Sargent Court. Here a varied association of artists and intellectuals, some of them immigrants from Russia, offered Sadakichi a very different milieu from that described by Gene Fowler in his *Minutes of the Last Meeting,* which recounts the activities of the Barrymore circle. It was here in this house, overlooking Elysian Park, that many artists — Ben Berlin, Raymond Brossard, Ronald Paintin, Einar Hansen, and others—often gathered for lively discussions and parties.

These were painters who he numbered among his "art children," just as there were many more in cities throughout the nation. The Detroit painter Marvin Beerbohm recalls that he and his wife "knew and loved Sadakichi from the time we first met him in 1934 in Detroit until his death." On his many visits to Detroit, Hartmann scolded, cajoled, and encouraged Beerbohm unceasingly. "As a struggling young painter and his wife, fighting the financial and cultural despair of the Depression years," writes Beerbohm, "we were proud to be numbered among Sadakichi's 'art children' of whom he had many across the country." Similarly, the Florida photographer, C. Verne Klintsworth, recalls it was Hartmann who first made him realize that photography was something much more than a commercial profession.

In the last six years of his life, Hartmann retreated to Catclaw Siding, a shack he built adjoining the home of his daughter, Wistaria Linton, on the Morongo Indian Reservation in Banning, California. There, he continued to paint pastels and write sporadically.

World War II imposed its horrors on the old man when the FBI started inquiring into his Japanese-German background, despite the fact that he had been a citizen since 1894. After they were interviewed by FBI agents, many of the Hollywood crowd quickly dropped Hartmann and invitations to parties ceased. Only Gene Fowler continued to show interest in the old man. In numerous embittered letters, Hartmann pleaded with high government officials not to intern him, arguing that there could be nothing more American than to have written the first modern *History of American Art*. The harassment never completely ceased, and sheriff's deputies again and again received reports from townspeople that Hartmann made periodic climbs to the top of Mt. San Jacinto to signal Japanese planes with a lantern.

In 1944, the 77-year-old Hartmann set out on his final journey east to visit another daughter, Dorothea Gilliland of St. Petersburg, Florida. He had in mind gathering material to complete his long unfinished autobiography, but instead he died in his daughter's home while sitting in a chair in November, the month of his birth.

In the first two decades of the twentieth century, Hartmann's reputation as an art critic appeared secure, and he was respected by men of stature such as Mencken, Huneker, Stieglitz, De Casseres, and Vance Thompson. One may well ask, therefore, why Hartmann has been so neglected? Much of the reason appears to lie in the unavailability of most of the publications for which Hartmann wrote and the lack of an edition of collected essays. Ezra Pound diagnosed such reasons for Hartmann's obscurity in his *Cantos*, placing Sadakichi as a member of the "lost legion" whose writings had disappeared in the "fly-by-night periodicals." Also militating against Hartmann would seem to be his deliberate cultivation of a literary pose to its ultimate conclusion — a grotesque caricature of the Bohemian artist.

Although there exists no biography of Hartmann or a definitive bibliography of his works, there are indications that historians and art critics are beginning to reevaluate this maverick of the seven arts. The first major recognition of Hartmann as one of our most durable and significant art critics was recorded by Jerome Mellquist in *The Emergence of an American Art* (Charles Scribner's Sons, 1942).

Mellquist termed Sadakichi "the indefatigable Hartmann" and "the unruly one," more formidable than Charles H. Caffin, whom he refers to as "the gentle critic." He sees Hartmann's most vigorous evaluations as appearing in the pages of *Camera Work*, where: "He estimated Day, Käsebier, Keiley, Eugene, and Stieglitz with sharpness and tact. And though he did not spare them, he did recognize that new blossoms were peeping out of the American soil." Given his honesty and precision, Hartmann inevitably became embroiled in disputes. He was in the midst of conflicts between both revolutionaries and counter-revolutionaries in art. One artist who caused dispute was Frank Eugene, whose experimentations in photography evoked howls of protest. Mellquist notes that, "Today, of course, one must agree with Sadakichi Hartmann, who said that he felt a 'strange vein of poetry,' a 'dreamy voluptousness,' and an 'amplitude of masses' in the pictures of Eugene. He scratched and kneaded and piled and thickened his material, until, by the time he got through, it was 'broken by speckles, flashes, passing shimmers and accidental light.' Perfectly delightful! In short, declared Hartmann, 'there is a sort of language in his 'muddiness' . . . His daubs and lines are vital.' "

Again, Mellquist notes that in contrast to other critics, the showing of the paintings of Alfred Mauer and Marin in March, 1909,, offered little difficulty to Hartmann: "Sadakichi Hartmann, a more supple critic and an upholder of the unconventional in art, summed it all up when he said that Mauer, having tired of brown and blue shadows, 'made the scarlet departure,' and 'introduced pink, crimson, and ruby-colored shadows."

Except by Hartmann, Max Weber, was at first universally received with negative criticism. Mellquist, reviewing the period, finds that "It was the gypsy Hartmann, writing later in *Camera Work*, who alone delivered an intelligent estimate. He detected in Weber's show 'architectural forms that, despite their extravagance and strangeness, impress us with an indescribable something such as we may feel before some old mural painting.' The much-challenged exhibition caused him no trouble at all: 'Weber' — and here he concluded — 'merely dissects the human form into geometrical ratios and color patterns and apparently proceeds like a primitive bent upon conquering his own knowledge of visual appearances.' This can still stand as an assessment of the painter." Over and over, Meliquist finds Hartmann to be a "pathfinder," who like Charles H. Caffin had already fulfilled himself as an art critic before World War I.

Mellquist enumerates manifold contributions of Hartmann, noting that among the pioneers who wrote for *Camera Work*, "some were raiders, some publicists, some poets, some satirists — all were engaged in a single battle, to crush prejudice . . . among the scouts and raiders none was more effective than Sadakichi Hartmann." He provides some sense of the varied resources of Hartmann: "Sometimes he merely darted forward on a swift foray, naming Pictorial Photography as a possible source of stimulation to interior decoration. Again he nimbly sketched Steichen's studio, or memorialized a suicide sculptor, John Donoghue. Still later he cast a strange fragrance as he wept over the death of Whistler in *White Chrysanthemums*. But the main charges of this restless intelligence were elsewhere. As early as 1903, in an essay entitled *The Value of the Apparently Meaningless and Inaccurate*, he unforgettably identified the magazine with an objection to the merely accurate in art. For, said he, 'the love for exactitude is the lowest form of pictorial gratification.' Thus he had already forecast the fighting-lines of a decade later."

Since Mellquist's analysis, others have begun to show interest in the man who in the early 1890's projected a new aesthetic for young American artists. Gene Fowler's *Minutes of The Last Meeting* presents a picture of the apocryphal Bohemian in his declining years. In 1963, the *World Encyclopedia of Art* omitted Huneker in its evaluation of art critics and listed only Hartmann and Caffin as the advanced critics of their period. Two years ago, the Japanese scholar Saburo Ota spent several months in this country, carrying out research on Hartmann, which was followed by a series of articles in the journal *Haiku*. A French journal has recently published some of Stephane Mallarme's correspondence with Hartmann. Barbara Rose's *Readings in American Art Since 1900* (1968) includes a selection of his essays. Mr. Harvey Hirsch, who lives in Michigan, has been collecting Hartmann materials for a long time and apparently plans a biographical study. *The Dictionary of American Biography* plans to include an article on Hartmann by Fred E. H. Schroeder of the University of Minnesota in its new edition. Dr. Peter C. Bunnell, Curator of Photography at the Museum of Modern Art, is engaged in critical study of Hartmann in connection with his studies of American photography. And in 1968, J. F. Burke published a novel titled *Noah* in which Sadakichi Hartmann appears as a major fictional character.

Much more might be said about this multifoliate life: the literary figures and coteries with whom Hartmann was associated; the many unpublished manuscripts of geniuine merit; the uncounted articles on an amazing variety of subjects, often written pseudonymously; and the published works long out of print and in need of collecting and editing. Eventually, Hartmann's intellectual and artistic achievements will be exhumed from the detritus of anecdotal apocrypha and fanciful lengendry. My fellow collaborator on Hartmann research, Harry Lawton, and I look upon this exhibit as one means of launching a much needed rediscovery and reconstruction. In addition, we have begun publication of the *Sadakichi Hartmann Newsletter* to facilitate communication between collectors, critics, and literary historians who are or who become interested in Hartmann's · *ouevres*. Perhaps the culminating work will be the biography which Hartmann's daughter and literary executrix, Mis. Wistaria Linton, has authorized.

Thus, this exhibition represents an introduction to an amazing man who held the banner of American art high and never compromised his artistic integrity. Sheridan Ford once tried to introduce Hartmann at a lecture as having never soiled the banner of art that he was carrying. "No," interrupted Hartmann, "Don't say that, rather say that it is soiled, shot full of holes, powder-stained, hanging in tatters, but that despite all he is still waving it, *morituri te salutant!*"

—*George Knox*
Department of English

Fabris: *Sadakichi*, 1931 (Cat. No. 102)

Prologue to Sadakichi

Sadakichi Hartmann is the youngest old man I have ever known. Not the adolescent youth of our times and our land where old women wear short skirts and old men dye their hair, but the youth which is eternal, which finds its way to the essential things.

There is a certain timelessness in Sadakichi's youth. He always appears to be of his time. Not because he is interested in the latest fad of the moment which appears to be our American way, but because he makes his way unerringly to the things in his time which have that vital quality in them which keeps them alive and young forever.

The other day I looked through Sadakichi's *History of American Art* which he wrote in 1900. I discovered there again, in turning over the leaves of his book that he had found and appreciated the true artists of that generation, the men who had been neglected by contemporary critics. I found there appreciation of Thomas Eakins, Albert Pinkham Ryder, and Winslow Homer, men who were then scarcely noticed. I even discovered a long and enthusiastic disquisition on the work of Alfred Stieglitz in photography. Who but Sadakichi Hartmann, among our critics, was writing about Tryon, Dewing, and Steichen in the years of 1893-1900? (And the artists whom he championed did they appreciate his courage and unerring discrimination? Surely not in a sense of material reciprocity.)

Sadakichi is certainly one of the most extraordinary characters which this century has produced. He has made contributions in criticism of the arts, in writing stories and poetry, in his reading of poetry, and in his dancing. Why then is he not better known and appreciated? The answer ,it seems to me, is simple. He is too much of an original for us Americans. He is one of the remarkable singulars who do not fit into our machine life. Gertrude Stein, who for all the peculiarities of her writing, is one of the wise women of our generation, has stated the case in her "Making of Americans," she says:

> "Yes, real singularity we have not made enough of yet so that any other one can really know it. I say vital singularity is as yet an unknown product with us, we who in our habits, dress-suit cases, clothes and hats and ways of thinking, walking, making money, talking, having simple lines in decorating, in ways of reforming, all with a metalic clicking like the typewriting which is our only way of thinking our way of educating our way of learning, all always the same way of doing, all the way down as far as there is any way down inside to us. We all are the same all through us, we never have it to be free inside us. No brother singulars, it is sad here for us, there is no place in an adolescent world for anything eccentric like us, machine making does not turn out queer things like us, they can never make a world to let us be free each one inside us."

I consider Sadakichi Hartmann one of the great singulars of all times!

Holger Cahill

Read before lecture, "Art by the Few for the Few," at Romany Marie's, New York, January 22, 1933.

W. M. Hollinger: *Sidney Allan,*
ca. 1905 (Cat. No. 107)

Sadakichi Hartmann, Art Critic

Pairs Herald, September, 1906

One of the strangest and most original men of letters of the day — in the United States at all events — is Sadakichi Hartmann, the poet, art critic, and lecturer. He was born in the land of wistarias and chrysanthemums, and he sees life with that Japanese anarchy of perspective.

His gifts are abundant and multiform, and his genius for writing has many modes and moods. He is lyric, naive and mystic, brutally realistic, dramatic at turns and for all that eminently oriental. He has written about the sea more musically than any poet of latter days. He has enriched the short story literature with a few pages of exquisite gray prose. He has written strange, flame colored dramas on the vanished gods — Buddha and Christ and Mohammed. And he has told the tragedy of a New York flat in the speech common on the East Side.

Not satisfied with these accomplishments, rare as they are fantastic, he has become the high-priest of American Art. Critically he has carried the American art movement on his shoulders for the last fifteen years. His courage is to be admired, though it is a vain ambition for a man "who has the poet's insight into life." Not that talented sculptors and painters are entirely absent in the land of Howells and Comstock, but they are deficient in red blood corpuscles. Artists have a hard life of it over there, and their work shows it. The trouble with American art is that it is hodden gray and anemic. And as their critic "the man with the Hokusai profile and broad Teutonic culture" (to quote J. G. Huneker) is, if anything at all, a strong natural man, the result is pallid and unprofitable. Nothing more sad than a critic who is more virile and vital than the work he criticizes.

With worthier subjects he might have dowered the world with more intellectual magnificence. Yet that is his affair. He for his part is sincere. He believes in American art and artists and carries his message to and fro the entire country.

He has compiled the first *History of American Art* (L. C. Page & Co., 1901 and Hutchinson & Co., London, 1903) and he was the first writer who succeeded in popularizing the peculiarities and beauties of Japanese art to us (L. C. Page & Co., Boston, 1903 and G. P. Putnam Sons, London, 1904). He was never prolific, brevity is his greatest charm and strength, and in a few essays, as "Color in Architecture," "Puvis de Chavannes," "The Flat Iron Building," "The Influence of Visual Perception on Technique," he has summed up some of the most important theories of modern art. In his "White Chrysanthemums," a prose poem of scarcely five hundred words he has laid down his entire art creed, "to learn to look at pictures as we look at the flush of the evening sky, at a passing cloud, at the vision of a beautiful woman, or at a white chrysanthemum."

He seems to have pondered deeply on Zola's epithet "art is a fragment of nature as seen through a temperament," and like wise Anatole France's "criticism is the adventure of one's soul among masterpieces" — and it seems to me almost to his undoing.

Criticism of this kind is no longer criticism, it is either appreciation or irony. His art writings are poetical, beautiful, visionary rather than analytical. Sadakichi Hartmann's contention is that this is the only way to reach the public, "to reflect by a new work of art the beauty of the original." "Why," he exclaimed one day to me "if a picture is really beautiful, one must be able to write a poem about it, or express it in music or any other art."

His style is peculiar, it reaches from slang to the academically *caduque*, it is chameleon-like, it adapts itself to every new subject; it is at once materialistic and mystic, emotional and matter of fact. I do not speak of his journalistic efforts. In them he is not better than the ordinary "art gentleman," but whenever he finds a subject to his liking, he saddles his Pegasus and gallops away to some Castillian fountain, where he may sit cross-legged in the twilight and meditate in oriental fashion upon the fugitive beauties of this world.

Withal his virtues as an art critic are non-literary. In other branches of literature, he is an innovator, a constructor of new forms. In his poems he combines the free verse with the most difficult metrical forms like the sestine and pantoum. His short stories advance one step beyond the French, in as far as they depict the influence of the momentary environment. In his dramas that remind one vaguely of Shelley and Ibsen's "Peer Gynt" he is at the mercy of an imagination which is neither to hold nor to bind.

His art criticisms on the other hand show the struggle of objective observaation and subjective interpretation, and the development of an individual style is handicapped thereby.

As I have said before his greatest virtues as an art critic are non-literary. And they are his broad and deep culture, his sincerity and astounding frankness, his fresh and personal sense of life and the enthusiasm of a singularly strong and attractive personality.

Vance Thompson

The Exhibition and Catalogue

Although *The Life and Times of Sadakichi Hartmann* presents the individual works of many American artists and photographers, it also strives to tell a story by assembling art and objects in such a manner as to create a biographical environment. Admittedly, this is a difficult objective and the viewer must decide for himself how successful the exhibition is in conveying Hartmann's unique personality, the variety and vicissitudes of his life, his dreams, successes, and failures.

The exhibition follows Hartmann's life chronologically, beginning with Raymond Brossard's flamboyant Cubist symbolization of *The Birth of Sadakichi* and ending with a gray and poignant rendering in oil of the aged Hartmann, painted shortly before his death, by Detroit artist Marvin Beerbohm. Interspersed with the works of artists and photographers who sought to capture the essential Hartmann are more than 500 mementos and artifacts of his career. These include a display of Hartmann's books and many unpublished manuscripts; correspondence from famous figures in the fields of literature and art; family photographs and albums; scrapbooks of news clippings (such as his German essays in the *New York Staats-Zeitung*); announcements and posters advertising lectures and performances; scarce *avant-garde* periodicals in which he published; and objects such as his Buddha incense burner, a favorite candlestick, and the ornate cloak he wore in *The Thief of Bagdad*.

A phantasmal glimpse into the private visions of Hartmann's mind is provided through the cooperation of Michael Shouff, who has created psychedelic light shows for the Iron Butterfly and other groups. One room adjoining the Library Gallery is devoted to Shouff's interpretation of Hartmann's outline for the first such light show, which appeared as Scene 12 of his drama *Buddha* (1897). It represents the first performance ever given of Hartmann's original light show, titled *Darkness in Space* or *Nirvana*.

Necessarily, the scope and impact of the exhibition cannot be properly reflected in this catalogue. Without extensive annotation, many of the objects and other materials displayed would have little meaning in a catalogue. Even with annotations, they would tend to crowd out and deemphasize the art works which are central to the exhibition. For that reason, the emphasis of this catalogue is upon the works of the many artists and photographers who depicted Hartmann.

Probably no American man of letters was so frequent a subject of painters, sculptors, and photographers as Sadakichi. As an art critic, much of his life was spent in their company, conducting interviews at their studios, lecturing to art groups, and serving continually as a judge of art and photographic shows.

Inevitably, artists of every school — impressionists, realists, cubists, and expressionists — were drawn to Hartmann as a subject, attracted as the sculptor Jo Davidson said by a face that "resembled a Japanese mask." Photographers from Zaida Ben Yusuf in 1894 to Edward Weston in the 1920's also sought to capture the many moods of his unusual features.

Hartmann, in turn, thoroughly enjoyed posing, often dropping sly hints to artists who were dilatory in asking him to sit. Frequently he gave talks to art classes while the students concentrated upon catching his exotic visage. A guest at one of Hartmann's lectures at the home of Isidore Schindler in Los Angeles in the 1930's remembers an evening that ended with a dozen or more artists sketching Sadakichi as he danced. The New York artist Raymond Brossard began his career with a one-man show of caricatures of Hartmann that drew praise from Arthur Millier.

In the months of effort that have gone into writing art museums, art historians, private collectors, and friends of Hartmann to bring together as many as possible of those works of art which depicted him, there have been triumphs, disappointments, and surprises. It may be hoped that this exhibition will be instrumental in bringing to light many more works that have vanished — paintings and drawings by Robert Henri, Ernest Lawson, Marcus Waterman, F. D. Marsh, Marius De Zayas and numerous others; the infuriatingly elusive Jo Davidson bust; and portraits by Clarence White, Frank Eugene, F. Holland Day and innumerable other photographic pioneers and innovators. Particularly disconcerting was the discovery that many art museums lack subject indexes or are prone to place non-contemporary art in storage without making adequate plans for retrieval.

More appalling has been our discovery that whole eras of American art history are endangered or being destroyed by art directors concerned only with juggling their holdings to keep pace with the mercurial tastes of their wealthier trustees. The works of that misfortune-haunted Cubist Ben Berlin have disappeared from several museums he selected as repositories of his paintings. Both a Decker and a Hanson appear in this catalogue through the courtesy of a collector who rescued them by purchase several weeks ago from what was nothing more than a rummage sale of works from the permanent holdings of a prominent California art museum. Other works were located in irretrievable disrepair in basements — or could not even be found in their present storage facilities. Several museums were unable to find the works of pioneer photographers donated many years ago by Hartmann even with the aid of the original accession documents. And Hartmann's best pastels no longer appear to exist in several museums in which he placed them — nor are there any records of their disposal to guide the searcher.

Nevertheless, it has been possible to assemble a representative collection of art works that present something of the quixotic spirit of Sadakichi. There are three oils by the Danish emigrant Ejnar Hansen, who studied at the Royal Academy of Arts, Copenhagen, and who was a member of the famous group called "The 13." Frode N. Dann described his treatment of Hartmann as "not just a recording of physical facts about a dramatic, colorful personality; it is psychoanalysis, derived from a natural gift of intuition and imagination." Peter Krasnow represents the poet-intellectual surrounded by sad mannikins which hint of Hartmann's need for adulation. Albert Rosenthal depicts a somber Sadakichi at the height of his critical reputation. John Decker captures, as Gene Fowler noted, "eyes of mystic agony" and a "face of a thousand sad secrets." There is also the portrait by C. E. Polowetski, who studied under Robert Blum and received the Prix d'Atelier at the Beaux Arts, and who was eulogized by William Rose Benet for his fluency, versatility, and sympathy toward his subjects. The caricaturists also are well represented: the decadent Leslie Cauldwell; Lillian Bonham, that good-humored mocker; and Raymond Brossard, who shows us Sadakichi the lunatic, gleeful charlatan and the compelling guru.

The photographers, whom Hartmann would permit "only a modest place in the graphic arts," are represented. Steichen, unrivaled, delineates a stolid and Teutonic Hartmann, almost a grim academic. Gertrude Käsebier portrays him as, if not yet a saint, then on the verge of sainthood. Bruguiere realizes in full what becomes a troublesome paradox — a fragile mysticism that is belied by a mouth and jaw that seem to contain all the cunning of a Boyar prince. Eickemeyer, on the other hand, gives us a wonderfully sensitive and arrogant Hartmann. There are also, of course, quite a few photographs by the omnipresent J. C. Strauss, the St. Louis brutalist, reputed to have photographed Hartmann more than 500 times and who Sadakichi once said "works his camera like a breech-loading gun."

In addition to the art works in which Hartmann appears as a subject, the exhibition also presents a selection of pastels by Sadakichi. In the early 1890's, Hartmann struggled with painting, studying at various art schools and under John Ward Stimson, not yet certain whether he would make his way eventually as an artist. He soon decided that he lacked a major talent and would regard his work as the past-time of an amateur, much as Thackeray looked upon his caricatures.

It was the painter A. B. Davies (later the force behind the Armory Show of 1912) who persuaded Hartmann to concentrate on pastels rather than oils. Hartmann saw his pastels as a continuous protest "against the tameness of the photographic tendency in art — doing things from nature without an especially subjective expression." His first show, titled "Impressions of an Amateur," was held at B. Kramer's Studio in New York in 1894. In 1900, his work was exhibited with that of Perrine, Glackens, Fuhr, and Lawrence in the Allan Gallery.

The bulk of Hartmann's best work in the media was produced in the 1890's and early 1900's. By 1896, he had sold almost a hundred pastels and given many away to friends. Purchasers included Parke Godwin, Daniel Huntington, Stanford White, Augustus St. Gaudens, and John Gellatly. Among those known to have received pastels as gifts were Stephane Mallarmé, Robert Henri, Brander Matthews, Gustav Verbeck, and Katherine Mayo. Only one pastel, *Garret-Splendor* (1893), is known to survive from this early period.

Blues and greens predominated in Hartmann's earliest pastels, and there was often a strange luminosity that some critics found almost religious. The New England poet Anne Throop wrote of Hartmann's pastels: "In these pictures, there is a marked strain of epicureanism, a fastidiousness seeking after the unconventionally beautiful. The figures and subjects are such as are rather dreamt of than seen. Naive figures of lovers, drawn almost in silhouettes, sitting on the seashore; lonesome figures of women, gazing at rivers floating by or over the sea at the setting sun, marines with a dashing surf in quaint violent colors; swans floating on glimmering lakes; squalls and storms."

The idea for a Sadakichi Hartmann exhibition originated in a conversation at the home of Hartmann's daughter by his second marriage, Mrs. Wistaria Linton, less than a year ago. Several persons, looking at the collection belonging to Mrs. Linton, were fascinated by the many portraits, photographs, and other materials in her possession. They were equally intrigued by the knowledge that there were other works by prominent artists and amateurs in private collections and art museums across the country.

Robert Lang, assistant librarian, thought it appropriate to attempt to assemble as many of these art works as could be located for an exhibition in the new University Library Gallery. The Riverside Press-Enterprise Co. agreed to serve as co-sponsors of the exhibition and to underwrite the catalogue. Chancellor Ivan Hinderaker generously provided a fund to help defray expenses involved in organizing the exhibit.

The task of officially supervising the show and publishing the catalogue was undertaken by Stephen Fry, music librarian and director of exhibits. His skilled assistant, Mrs. Joyce Klure, was responsible for arrangement and planning of the exhibition. Assisting in locating art work and in the preparation of the catalogue were Mrs. Linton, literary executrix of her father's estate, and George Knox and Harry Lawton, editors for the estate, who are currently working on a Hartmann biography. Bibliographical assistance on the catalogue was provided by Michael Elderman. Providing help with photo-reproduction for the catalogue was John Bosak. Victoria Lerman rendered editing help.

In addition to the many lenders, appreciation must be expressed to the following other persons who provided assistance in a multitude of ways: Howard H Hays, Jr., editor and co-publisher of the Press-Enterprise Co.; Vernon Tegland of Rubidoux Printing Co.; Charles Stiles of the Press-Enterprise Co.; Donald W. Ward, head of photo services in the library; Beaumont Newhall of Eastman House, Rochester, New York; Peter Goldschmidt of the University of California Office, Washington, D.C.; Raymond Brossard of New York City; Mrs. Dorothea Gilliland of St. Petersburg, Florida; Larry Curry, curator of history at Los Angeles County Art Museum; Nick Briganti of the Los Angeles County Art Association; Joshua C. Taylor, director of the National Collection of Fine Arts, Washington, D.C.; Peter Bunnell, curator of photography for the Museum of Modern Art, New York City; Mrs. Benita Korn, Brooklyn; and Neil Barron, assistant librarian at Sacramento State College.

—*Harry Lawton*

Lenders to the Exhibition

Joe and Dixie Allen, La Crescenta
Peter Bunnell, New York, N.Y.
Marvin Beerbohm, Detroit, Mich.
Raymond Brossard, New York, N.Y.
Boris Deutsch, Los Angeles
Michael Elderman, Riverside
Will Fowler, Encino
Dorothea Gilliland, St. Petersburg, Fla.
J. Cozzy Graham
Murray Gribin, Los Angeles
Mrs. Ejnar Hansen, Pasadena
Edgar Hartmann, Tucson, Ariz.
Paul Hartmann, St. Petersburg, Fla.
Richard F. Hill, Redington Beach, Fla.
Peter Krasnow, Los Angeles
C. Verne Klintworth, Tampa, Fla.
Karl H. Kretschmar, Fraser, Mich.
Charlotte Lance, Ridley Park, Pa.
Harry Lawton, Riverside
Library of Congress, Washington, D.C.
Library Company of Philadelphia
    Philadelphia, Pa.
Wistaria Hartmann Linton, Riverside
Marigold Linton, San Diego
California Exposition and Fair,
    Sacramento
Sidney Morse, Hollywood
Oakland Municipal Art Museum,
    Oakland
Riverside Public Library, Riverside
Virginia Scott, Pasadena
William Stelling, New York, N.Y.
David Stone, Long Beach
Harry Weber, Los Angeles

Eugene: *Portrait of Elizabeth Blanche Walsh*, *ca.* 1896 (Cat. No. 102)

Catalogue of the Exhibition*

PASTELS AND PHOTOGRAPHS BY SADAKICHI HARTMANN

1. *Garret-Splendor*, 1893
   Pastel, 9½ x 7½

2. *A Conversation with Walt Whitman*, 1895
   Photocopy of pen and ink caricature, 8¼ x 12½

3. *Elizabeth Blanche Hartmann*. 1896
   Photograph, 7 x 9¼

4. *Elizabeth Blanche Hartmann at Studio 16*, 1896
   Photograph, 6½ x 4½
   Lent by Dorothea Gilliland

5. *Reincarnation*, 1914
   Pastel, 11½ x 8

6. *The Shore of Drifting Sand*, 1914
   Set design for Scene I of *Buddha*
   Pastel, 9 x 11¾

7. *On the Banks of the Ganges*, 1914
   Set design for Scene II of *Buddha*
   Pastel, 9 x 11¾

8. *A Village Street*, 1914
   Set design for Scene III of *Buddha*
   Pastel, 9 x 11¾

9. *The Temple of Renunciation*, 1914
   Set design for Scene IV of *Buddha*
   Pastel, 9 x 11¾

10. *A Battlefield*, 1914
    Set design for Scene V of *Buddha*
    Pastel, 9 x 11¾

11. *At the Forest's Edge of Life*, 1914
    Set design for Scene VII of *Buddha*
    Pastel, 9 x 11¾

12. *The Vale of Rest*, 1914
    Set design for Scene VIII of *Buddha*
    Pastel, 9 x 11¾

13. *The Cave of Dawn*, 1914
    Set design for Scene IX of *Buddha*
    Pastel, 9 x 11¾

14. *At the Boundary of Perpetual Snow*, 1914
    Set design for Scene X of *Buddha*
    Pastel, 9 x 11¾

15. *Summit of the Himalayas*, 1914
    Set design for Scene XI of *Buddha*
    Pastel, 9 x 11¾

16. *Lillian*, 1916
    (Portrait of his second wife, Lillian Bonham Hartmann)
    Photograph, 11 x 8½

17. *Wistaria*, ca. 1916
    (Portrait of his daughter)
    Photograph, 9¼ x 5¾

18. Untitled multiple exposure composition of his daughters, Wistaria and Marigold, ca. 1917
    Photograph, 7½ x 9½

19. *Mission Church and Graveyard*, ca. 1923
    Pastel, 8½ x 11½
    Lent by the Elizabeth French Collection

20. *Self-Portrait*, 1927
    Photograph, 12½ x 9

21. *Moon Over Mt. San Jacinto*, ca., 1938
    Pastel, 9 x 12

*All works in the exhibition for which the lender is not identified are from the Wistaria Hartmann Linton collection. In the case of undated works, it has proven impossible to ascribe even an approximate date.

22. *The Wandering Jew*
Pastel, 9 x 11¾

23. *Lake Tranquility*
Pastel, 8¾ x 11½

24. *Quelle Heure Est'il?*
Pastel, 8¾ x 11½

25. *Baker Eddy as a Young Girl*
Pastel, 11½ x 8¾

26. *Baker Eddy at Columbus Avenue*
Pastel, 11¾ x 8¾

27. *The Acrobat*
Pastel, 8½ x 9½

28. *Once I Lived There*
Pastel, 10¼ x 11

29. *An American Tragedy*
Pastel, 12 x 8¾

30. *Woodland*
Pastel, 7½ x 12

31. *Autumn Scenery*
Pastel, 6¾ x 19½

32. *Crystal*
Pastel, 15½ x 11¾

33. *An Old Story*
Pastel, 10½ x 11¾

34. *The Seven Veils*
Pastel, 14 x 11

35. *The Acrobat and the Magician*
Pastel, 11¾ x 9

36. *The Redheaded Woman*
Pastel, 11½ x 10¼

THE WORKS OF OTHER ARTISTS

37. Marvin Beerbohm
Sadakichi Hartmann, 1940
Oil on canvas, 42 x 32
Lent by Marvin Beerbohm
(The last oil painting ever
made of Hartmann)

38. Ben Berlin
Opus to Sadakichi, 1934
(Photograph of the lost
70 by 70 pastel)

39. Ben Berlin
Margery Winter, 1935
Oil on canvas, 13½ x 12
Lent by Harry Weber

40. Lillian Bonham
Self-Portrait, ca. 1908
Watercolor, 17 x 11¼

41. Lillian Bonham
Art in Denver is a Rarity, ca. 1913
Pen and ink, 14¾ x 10

42. Lillian Bonham
Sadakichi-Pierrot, ca. 1912
Pen and ink, 8 x 5

43. Lillian Bonham
Social Lion, ca. 1912
Pen and ink, 8 x 5

44. Lillian Bonham
The Critic, ca. 1912
Pen and ink, 8 x 5

45. Lillian Bonham
*Sadakichi with Confucius, Christ,
and Buddha at the Bar*, ca. 1915
Postcard of pen and ink, 3½ x 5½
Lent by Dorothea Gilliland

46. Lillian Bonham
*Thanks Owes to Sadakichi the
Nation, for the Steady Increase in
Population*, ca. 1915
Postcard of pen and ink, 3½ x 5½
Lent by Dorothea Gilliland

47. Lillian Bonham
*First Ibsen Performance in Bos-
ton*, ca. 1915
Postcard of pen and ink, 5½ x 3½
Lent by Dorothea Gilliland

48. Lillian Bonham
Symphony Domestica, ca. 1915
Postcard of pen and ink, 5½ x 3½
Lent by Dorothea Gilliland

49. Lillian Bonham
Oh Why is This World So Full of Care? Sadakichi Says Because Schopenhauer is in the Air, ca. 1915
Postcard of pen and ink, 5½ x 3½
Lent by Dorothea Gilliland

50. Lillian Bonham
Sadakichi Trying Hard to be a Great Man Went Frying Eggs with the Great Walt Whitman, ca. 1915
Postcard of pen and ink, 5½ x 3½
Lent by Dorothea Gilliland

51. Lillian Bonham
The Asthma Dog, ca. 1915
Postcard of pen and ink, 5½ x 3½
Lent by Dorothea Gilliland

52. Lillian Bonham
Sadakichi Teaching Delsarte, ca. 1915
Postcard of pen and ink, 5½ x 3½
Lent by Dorothea Gilliland

53. Lillian Bonham
The Modern Omar, ca. 1915
Postcard of pen and ink, 5½ x 3½
Lent by Dorothea Gilliland

54. Lillian Bonham
Sadakichi Reading Poe, ca. 1915
Postcard of pen and ink, 5½ x 3½
Lent by Dorothea Gilliland

55. Lillian Bonham
Henry Clews in Diga t,ca. 1915
Postcard of pen and ink, 5½ x 3½
Lent by Dorothea Gilliland

56. Lillian Bonham
Walt Whitman, ca. 1918
Photograph of bas relief

57. Raymond Boynton
Sketch of Sadakichi Hartmann dancing on fly-leaf of book
Pencil, 8 x 5½
Lent by Athene Roberts

58. Raymond Brossard
Untitled sketches of S.H., *ca.* 1935
Pen and ink, 11¼ x 14½
Lent by Harry Weber

59. Raymond Brossard,
Sadakichi Thinking of Heliogabalus, 1969
Watercolor and pen and ink, 15½ x 11
Lent by Harry Lawton

60. Raymond Brossard
Untitled sketches of Margery Winter, 1935
Pencil and chalk, 19½ x 14
Lent by Harry Weber

61. Raymond Brossard
Untitled sketches of S.H., *ca.* 1935
Pen and ink, 8¾ x 14
Lent by Harry Weber

62. Raymond Brossard
Sadakichi Hartmann, 1935
Pen and ink, 11½ x 8¼
Lent by the artist

63. Raymond Brossard
Margery Winter, 1935
Pencil, 9 x 7
Lent by Harry Weber

64. Raymond Brossard
Reflections in Ink of Sadakichi, With Apologies to Amadeo Modigliani, 1969
Pen and ink, 16 x 10
Lent by the artist

65. Raymond Brossard
*Dreaming of the Sadakichi Hart-
mann Bar in Saigon*, 1969
Pen and ink, 12½ x 9
Lent by the artist

66. Raymond Brossard
Sadakichi Hartmann, 1969
Ink and wax crayon collage,
9 x 11½
Lent by Michael J. Elderman

67. Raymond Brossard
Sadakichi, 1969
Ink and mixed media, 14¾ x 10½
Lent by the artist

68. Raymond Brossard
Sadakichi, 1969
Mixed media, 10½ x 12¼
Lent by the artist

69. Raymond Brossard
Cubist Portrait of Sadakichi, 1935
Pastel, 11¼ x 8½

70. Raymond Brossard
The Birth of Sadakichi, 1935
Pastel, 34 x 26

71. Raymond Brossard
Sadakichi Hartmann, 1969
Pen and ink, 12½ x 9
Lent by the artist

72. Raymond Brossard
Good Friday, 1934
Enamel paint on wood,
14¾ x 11¾

73. Leslie Cauldwell
Cariacature of Sadakichi, ca. 1894
Photocopy of pastel, 6¾ x 3½

74. John Decker
Sadakichi Hartmann, 1940
Oil on canvas, 20 x 16½
Lent by Virginia Scott

75. John Decker
Sadakichi Hartmann, Portrait,
1940
Photocopy of original oil,
15½ x 18

75a. John Decker
Sadakichi, 1940
Colored pen and ink caricature
15 x 19½
Lent by Will Fowler

76. Boris Deutsch
*Hartmann Reading Poe at Schind-
lers*, 1928
Pen and ink
Lent by the artist

77. E. Gordigiani
Untitled portrait of S. H., 1897
Photocopy of pencil sketch,
18½ x 14½

78. Ejnar Hansen
To Sadakichi Hartmann, 1938
Pencil, 15 x 11
Lent by Edgar Hartmann

79. Ejnar Hansen
Sadakichi, 1932
Pencil, 20 x 15¾

80. Ejnar Hansen
Sadakichi, 1935
Plaster bust, 13 inches in height
Lent by Mrs. Ejnar Hansen

81. Ejnar Hansen
Sadakichi Hartmann, 1932
Oil on canvas, 50 x 40
Lent by Mrs. Ejnar Hansen

82. Ejnar Hansen
The Old Philosopher, 1940
Oil on canvas, 30 x 25
Lent by Mrs. Ejnar Hansen

83. Ejnar Hansen
Twilight of Sadakichi, 1943
Oil on canvas, 40 by 30
Lent by California Exposition

84. Paul Kangas
Sadakichi, 1937
Ceramic bust, 8 inches in height

85. Peter Krasnow
*Sadakichi Reading His Poetry to
an Invalid*, 1929
Oil on canvas, 23½ x 28
Lent by the artist

86. Peter Krasnow
Sadakichi Hartmann, ca. 1930
Pastel, 17¾ x 13½
Lent by Murray Griben

87. Peter Krasnow
*Sadakichi Reading His Poetry to
Young People*, 1929
Pastel, 21 x 17
Lent by the artist

88. Peter Krasnow
*Sadakichi Reading Poe at Schind-
ler's*, 1928
Lithograph, 15¾ x 10½
Lent by the artist

89. Alfredo Orselli
Sadakichi and the Muses, 1940
Charcoal, 18½ x 18½

90. Charles E. Polowetski
Sadakichi Hartmann, 1935
Oil on canvas, 30¾ x 24¼
*Lent by Oakland Municipal Art
Museum*

91. John Emerson Roberts
Sadakichi, 1934
Oil on canvas, 20 x 18
Lent by Joe Allen

92. Albert Rosenthal
Sadakichi Hartmann, ca. 1921
Oil on canvas, 29½ x 24½

93. F. H. Tompkins
C. Sadakichi Hartmann, 1893
Reproduction of pencil sketch,
12½ x 10½

94. Unknown Sculptor
Bas-relief of head of S.H.
Painted plaster, 5½ x 4

SADAKICHI
TRYING HARD TO BE
A GREAT MAN, WENT
FRYING EGGS WITH THE GREAT WHITMAN

Gordigiani: *Portrait*, 1897 (Cat. No. 77)

Tompkins: *C. Sadakichi
Hartmann*, 1893 (Cat. No. 93)

Cauldwell: *Caricature*,
1894 (Cat. No. 73)

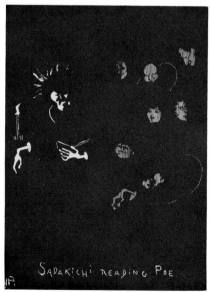

Bonham: *Two caricatures, ca.* 1915 (Cat. Nos. 54, 49)

Hartmann: A *Conversation with Walt Whitman*, 1895 (Cat. No. 2)

Bonham: *Self-Portrait,*
ca. 1908 (Cat. No. 40)

Hartmann: *The Wandering Jew* (Cat. No. 22)

Deutsch: *Hartmann Reading
Poe at Schindler's,* 1935
(Cat. No. 76)

Decker: *Sadakichi Hartmann, Portrait*, 1940 (Cat. No. 75)

Brossard: *Reflections in Ink* of Sadakichi with Apologies *to Amadeo Modigliani*, 1969 (Cat. No. 64)

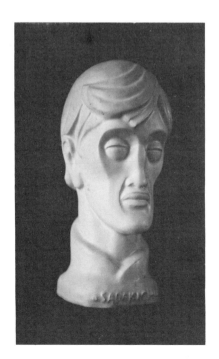

Kangas: *Sadakichi*, 1937 (Cat. No. 84)

Polowetski: *Sadakichi Hartmann, ca.* 1912 (Cat. No. 90)

Berlin: *Opus to Sadakichi*, 1934 (Cat. No. 38)

Hansen: *Sadakichi*, 1932 (Cat. No. 80)

To Sadakichi Hartmann
with best wishes from
Einar H.

Einar Hansen
1938

Hansen: *Sadakichi*, 1938 (Cat. No. 79)

Brossard: *The Birth of Sadakichi,* 1935 (Cat. No. 70)

Hartmann: *Garret-Splendor,*
1893 (Cat. No. 1)

Hartmann: *The Acrobat and the
Magician* (Cat. No. 35)

Hartmann: *The Redheaded
Woman* (Cat. No. 36)

Rosenthal: *Sadakichi Hartmann, ca.* 1912 (Cat. No. 92)

Hansen: *The Old Philosopher,*
1940 (Cat. No. 82)

Brossard: *Cubist Portrait,*
1935 (Cat. No. 69)

Krasnow: *Sadakichi Reading His Poetry to an Invalid*, 1929 (Cat. No. 85)

Krasnow: *Sadakichi Reading His Poetry to Young People*, 1929 (Cat. No. 87)

Decker: *Sadakichi Hartmann,*
1940 (Cat. No. 74)

Brossard: *Sadakichi Thinking
of Heliogabalus,* 1969
(Cat. No. 59)

Hansen: *Sadakichi Hartmann,* 1932 (Cat. No. 81)

Beerbohm: *Sadakichi Hartmann*, 1940 (Cat. No. 37)

PHOTOGRAPHS

95. Howard D. Beach
Untitled portrait of S.H., 1914
10 x 8

96. Zaida Ben Yusuf
Sidney Allan, 1898
7 x 4

97. Lillian Bonham
Untitled portrait of S.H. and his daughters, Marigold and Wistaria, taken at Elbert Hubbard's Roycroft Colony, 1915
Pastel on photograph, 19 x 26

98. Francis Bruguiere
Untitled portrait of S.H., ca. 1917
10 x 8

99. Francis Bruguiere
Untitled portrait of S.H., ca. 1917
13½ x 10½

100. B. Buehrman
Untitled portrait of S.H., ca. 1907
9¼ x 7¼

101. Rudolph Eickemeyer
Sadakichi Hartmann, ca. 1900
9 x 6½

102. Alfred Fabris
Untitled portrait of S.H., 1931
6½ x 4½

103. B. J. Falk
Sadakichi Hartmann, ca. 1899
3½ x 4½

104. B. J. Falk
For a Beloved Vagabond, ca. 1899
5½ x 4

105. Paul Fournier
Sadakichi Hartmann, 1907
6½ x 4¾

106. Harris & Ewing Studio
Hieroglyphics of Experience, 1937
9 x 7

107. W. M. Hollinger
Sidney Allan, ca. 1905
5 x 4

108. York Honore
Sadakichi Hartmann, the Story Teller, ca. 1930
Reproduction, 6½ x 5
Lent by J. Cozzy Graham

109. Gertrude Käsebier
Portrait of Sadakichi Hartmann, ca. 1910
Platinum print, 9¼ x 7¼
Lent by Peter C. Bunnell

110. C. Verne Klintworth, F.P.S.A.
Sadakichi, Typical Pose, 1923
18¼ x 13½
Lent by the photographer

111. C. Verne Klintworth, F.P.S.A.
Sadakichi - The Mask, 1923
18 x 14¼
Lent by the photographer

112. Harry Lawton
Matt Moore the Actor, 1954
7 x 5¾
Lent by the photographer

113. Wistaria Hartmann Linton
The Building of Catclaw Siding, 1938
8¾ x 13½

114. Wistaria Hartmann Linton
The Armchair Philosopher, 1940
13¾ x 10½

115. Wistaria Hartmann Linton
Looking Down the Road for Visitors Who Do Not Come, 1943

116. Wistaria Hartmann Linton
Hat, Coat, and Shoes, 1943

117. Wistaria Hartmann Linton
The Last Photograph, 1944
11¾ x 9¼

118. J. Ernest Mock
*Portrait of Sadakichi Hartmann,
ca.* 1930
6½ x 5
Lent by J. Cozzy Graham

119. J. Ernest Mock
Untitled portrait of S.H., 1913
9½ x 7

120. Charles L. Peck
Portrait of Lillian Bonham, ca.
1915
6 x 4¼
Lent by Marigold Linton

121. Edward Steichen
Sadakichi Hartmann, ca. 1905
Reproduction of photograph
from *Camera Work*
16 x 5¾

122. Stockton (Hollywood Studio)
Untitled portrait of S.H., ca.
1925
13¾ x 11½

123. J. C. Strauss
*Sadakichi Hartmann on a Ped-
estel,* 1896
10 x 5 (Cover Photo)

124. J. C. Strauss
Untitled portrait of S.H., ca.
1905
9¼ x 7

125. J. C. Strauss
*Untitled photograph of Strauss
and Hartmann taken by bulb re-
lease, ca.* 1905
9¼ x 6

126. J. C. Strauss
Sidney Allan, ca. 1906
7 x 4¼

127. J. C. Strauss
*Untitled portrait of Sidney Allan,
ca.* 1908
10 x 7½

128. J. C. Strauss
*Untitled portrait of Sadakichi
Hartmann,* 1911
7¾ x 6½

129. C. Warrington
*Sadakichi Hartmann as Court
Magician,* 1923
Still photograph from *The Thief
of Bagdad*
12¼ x 8½

130. C. Warrington
The Court Magician, 1923
Still photograph from *The Thief
of Bagdad*
10 x 13

131. Cliff Wesselmann
*What Weather Is It in the
World Today? ca.* 1938
13 x 8½

132. Cliff Wesselmann
Untitled outdoor portrait, ca.
1938
6¾ x 4¾

133. Cliff Wesselmann
A Novel Opening, ca. 1938
3 x 4½

134. Cliff Wesselmann
*How Your Father Looks When
He Thinks of All the Racial and
Religious Prejudices in the
World, ca.* 1940
6½ x 5

135. Cliff Wesselmann
Color portrait of S.H., 1938
Dye-transfer print, 9¼ x 7½

136. Unknown Photographer
Anne Throop, ca. 1895
(The New England poet)
9½ x 6

137. Unknown Photographer
Sadakichi Shaking Hands with John Burroughs, 1920
9 x 7½

138. Unknown Photographer
Sadakichi as "Oswald" in Ibsen's Ghosts, 1917
8¾ x 6½

139. Unknown Photographer
Lecturing, ca. 1935
9½ x 3¾

140. Unknown Photographer
Sadakichi Reading the California Demokrat, ca. 1910

141. Unknown Photographer
The Two Hamlets, 1940
(Sadakichi Hartmann and John Barrymore)
9½ x 7¾

142. Unknown Photographer
Sadakichi Laying a Wreath on Robert Louis Stevenson's Memorial, Portmouth Square, San Francisco, ca. 1916
10½ x 6½

143. Unknown Photographer
Margery Winter and Ben Berlin, ca., 1935
7½ x 9½
Lent by Harry Webber

144. Unknown Photographer
Osada Hartmann, ca. 1867
4¼ x 3¾

145. Unknown Photographer
Oscar Hartmann, n.d.
9¼ x 6

146. Unknown Photographer
Sadakichi Hartmann at the Age of 13, 1880
5½ x 3½

147. Unknown Photographer
C. Sadakichi Hartmann, 1889
4 x 5½

148. Unknown Photographer
The Court Magician and the Peacock, 1923
Still photograph from *The Thief of Bagdad*
7 x 9

149. Unknown Photographer
Scene from The Thief of Bagdad, 1923
9 x 12

Osada Hartmann, 1867
(Cat. No. 144)

Oscar Hartmann, n.d.
(Cat. No. 145)

Sadakichi Hartmann at the Age of 13,
1880 (Cat. No. 146)

C. Sadakichi Hartmann, 1889 (Cat. No. 147)

Hartmann: *Elizabeth Blanche Hartmann at Studio 16*, 1896
(Cat. No. 3)

Ben Yusuf: *Sidney Allan*, 1898
(Cat. No. 96)

Anne Throop, ca., 1896
(Cat. No. 136)

Eickemeyer: *Sadakichi Hartmann, ca.*, 1900 (Cat. No. 101)

Strauss: *Sidney Allan, ca.,* 1906
(Cat. No. 126)

Strauss: *Strauss and Hartmann, ca.* 1905 (Cat. No. 125)

Falk: *Sadakichi Hartmann,*
ca., 1899 (Cat. No. 103)

Fournier: *Sadakichi Hartmann,*
1917 (Cat. No. 105)

Sadakichi Reading the California Demokrat, ca., 1910 (Cat. No. 140)

Strauss: *Sadakichi*, 1911, 7¾ x 6½ (Cat. No. 128)

Käsebier: *Portrait of Sadakichi Hartmann, ca.,* 1910
Collection of Peter C. Bunnell (Cat. No. 109)

Peck: *Lillian Bonham Hartmann,*
ca. 1915 (Cat. No. 120)

Beach: *Untitled portrait*, 1914 (Cat. No. 95)

Bruguiere: *Untitled portrait,*
ca. 1917 (Cat. No. 99)

Bruguiere: *Untitled portrait,*
ca. 1917 (Cat. No. 98)

Sadakichi Shaking Hands With John Burroughs, 1920
(Cat. No. 137)

Klintworth: *Sadakichi, Typical Pose*, 1923 (Cat. No. 110)

*Sadakichi Laying a Wreath on Robert Louis
Stevenson's Memorial, ca.* 1916 (Cat. No. 142)

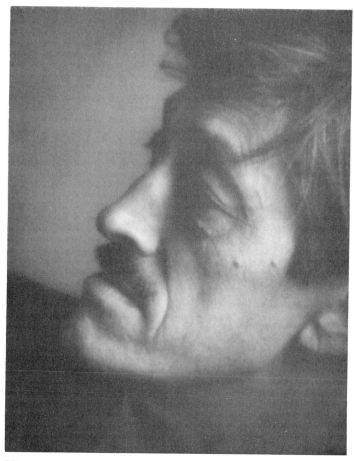

Klintworth: *Sadakichi—The Mask*, 1923 (Cat. No. 111)

Warrington: *The Court Magician*, 1923 (Cat. No. 130)

Scene from the Thief of Bagdad, 1923 (Cat. No. 149)

Stockton: *Untitled portrait, ca.* 1925 (Cat. No. 122)

Honore: *Sadakichi Hartmann,*
the Story Teller, ca. 1930
(Cat. No. 108)

Mock: *Portrait of Sadakichi*
Hartmann, ca. 1930
(Cat. No. 118)

The Two Hamlets, 1940
(Cat. No. 141)

Linton: *The Building of Catclaw Siding*, 1938 (Cat. No. 113)

Lecturing, ca., 1921
(Cat. No. 139)

Wesselmann: *How Your Father*
Looks When He Thinks of All
the Racial and Religious
Prejudices in the World, 1932
(Cat. No. 134)

Linton: *Looking Down the Road
for Visitors Who Do Not Come,*
1943 (Cat. No. 115)

A Selected Hartmann Bibliography

BOOKS AND PAMPHLETS

Allan, Sidney. *Composition in Portraiture*. New York: Edward L. Wilson, 1909.

Hartmann, Sadakichi. *A History of American Art*. 2 Vols. Boston: L. C. Page & Co. Publishers, 1901.

————. *A History of American Art*. Revised one volume ed. New York: Tudor Publishing Co., 1934. Includes a new final chapter by Hartmann, "An Art Wrangler's Aftermath."

————. *A Note on the Portraits of Walt Whitman*. New York: At the sign of the Sparrow, 1921.

————. *Conversations With Walt Whitman*. New York: E. P. Coby, 1895.

————. *Japanese Art*. Boston: L. C. Page & Co., 1903; London: G. P. Putnam's Sons, 1904.

————. *Landscape and Figure Composition*. New York: The Baker Taylor Company, 1910.

————. *The Last 30 Days of Christ*. New York: Privately Printed, 1920.

————., ed., *Modern American Sculpture*. New York: The Architectural Book Publishing Company, 1918.

————. *My Crucifixion: Asthma For 40 Years*. Author's edition. Tujunga, California: Printed at the Cloister Press, Hollywood, 1931.

————. *My Rubaiyat*. St. Louis, Missouri: Mangan Publishing Co. Author's Edition, 1913.

————. *My Rubaiyat*. Third revised edition. San Francisco: Privately printed, 1916.

————. *My Theory of Soul Atoms*. New York: The Stylus Publishing Co., 1910.

————. *Our Last Walk Together (In Memoriam Marigold Hartmann)*. Unpublished private edition, limited to 60 copies, 1921.

————. *Passport to Immortality*. Beaumont, California: Author's edition, 1927.

————. *Schopenhauer in the Air*. New York: Author's edition, 1899.

————. *Schopenhauer in the Air. Twelve Stories*. 2nd edition. Rochester, New York: The Stylus Publishing Co., 1908.

————. *Seven Short Stories*. Beaumont, California: Author's edition, limited to 500 copies, 1930.

————. *Shakespeare in Art*. Boston: L. C. Page & Co., 1901. Part of the "Art Lovers' Series."

————. *Strands and Ravelings of the Art Fabric*. Hollywood, California: Author's edition, 1940.

————. *Tanka and Haikai, Japanese Rhythms*. San Francisco: Author's edition, 1916.

————. *Tanka and Haikai, Japanese Rhythms*. Script edition, calligraphy by John C. Catlin, 1920.

————. *The Whistler Book: A Monograph of the Life and Position in Art of James McNeill Whistler, together with a Careful Study of His More Important Works*. Boston: L. C. Page & Co., 1910.

————. *The Whistler Book*. New Edition. Boston: L. C. Page & Co., 1924.

PLAYS

Buddha (Written 1891-95): *A Drama in Twelve Scenes*. New York: Author's edition, 1897. American edition limited to 100.

Christ, A Dramatic Poem in Three Acts. Boston: Privately printed, 1893.

Confucius, A Drama in Two Acts. Los Angeles, California: Privately printed, 1923.

Moses, A Drama in Six Episodes. Author's Photostat Edition, 1934.

A Tragedy in a New York Flat. A Dramatic Episode in Two Scenes. New York: The Author, 1896.

*Note: Two other religious plays, *Mohammed* and *Baker Eddy*, have not been published.

MAGAZINES

Hartmann, Sadakichi, ed. *Art Critic: Devoted to the Advancement of Interests of American Art*. Three issues, 1893-94.

————. *Art News*. Four issues, 1897.

————. *The Stylus*. Three issues, 1910.

ARTICLES ON PHOTOGRAPHY

Allan, Sidney. "A New Departure in Photography." *The Lamp*, XXVIII, No. 1 (Feb., 1904), pp. 19-25.

————. "Eduard J. Steichen, Painter, Photographer." *Camera Notes*, VI (1902), p. 1.

————. "The Exhibition of the Photo-Secession." *Photographic-Times Bulletin*, XXXVI (1904), pp. 132-133.

————. "The Flat-Iron Building—An Esthetical Dissertation." *Camera Work*, No. 4 (Oct., 1903), pp. 36-40.

————. "The Influence of Artistic Photography on Interior Decoration." *Camera Work*, No. 2 (April, 1903), pp. 31-33.

————. "The Influence of Visual Perception on Conception and Technique." *Camera Work*, No. 3 (July, 1903), pp. 23-26.

————. "Roaming in Thought" (After reading Maeterlinck's Letter). *Camera Work*, No. 4 (Oct., 1903), pp. 21-24.

————. "The Value of the Apparently Meaningless and Inaccurate." *Camera Work*, No. 3 (July, 1903), pp. 17-21.

————. "A Visit to Steichen's Studio." *Camera Work*, No. 2 (April, 1903), pp. 25-28.

————. "White Backgrounds." *American Annual of Photography*, XXIX (1915), pp. 218-221.

Eickemeyer, Rudolf, Jr. *Winter, Pictured by Rudolf Eickemeyer, Jr.* "Introduction" by Sadakichi Hartmann. New York: R. H. Russell, 1903.

Hartmann, Sadakichi. "The American Picture World, Its Shows and Shams." *Forum*, XLIV, No. 9 (Sept., 1910), pp. 295-304.

Hartmann, Sadakichi. "The Broken Plates." *Camera Work*, No. 6 (April, 1904), pp. 35-39.

————. "A Monologue." *Camera Work*, No. 6 (April, 1904), p. 25.

————. "The Camera in a Country Lane." *Scribner's Magazine*, XXXI, No. 6 (June, 1902), pp. 679-88. Photos by Rudolf Eickemeyer, Jr.

————. "Children as They are Pictured." *Cosmopolitan*, XLIII (July, 1907), pp. 235-47.

————. "Frederick I. Monsen." *Photographic Times*, XLI (1909), p. 79.

————. "German Practitioner: A. Gottheil of Danzig." *Photo-Era*, XXXIV (Feb., 1915), pp. 54-59.

————. "On the Lack of Culture." *Camera Work*, No. 6 (April, 1904), pp. 19-22.

————. "On the Vanity of Appreciation." *Camera Work*, No. 5 (Jan., 1904), pp. 21-23.

————. "The Photo-Secession Exhibition at the Carnegie Art Galleries, Pittsburgh, Pa." *Camera Work*, No. 6 (April, 1904), pp. 47-51.

————. "A Plea For Straight Photography." *American Amateur Photographer*. March, 1904, pp. 101-08.

————. "Pretty Women in Photography." *Cosmopolitan*, XLIII (May, 1907), pp. 3-15.

————. "A Reverie at the Seashore." *Harper's Monthly Magazine*, CV, No. DCXXVIII (Sept., 1902), pp. 561-68.

————. "What Remains." *Camera Work*, No. 33 (Jan., 1911), pp. 30-32.

————. "Why Was Rembrandt?" *American Annual of Photography*, XXX (1916), pp. 144-47.

ARTICLES ON OTHER ARTS

"Albert Pinkham Ryder." *Magazine of Art*, XXXI, No. 9 (Sept., 1938), pp. 500-03, 550-51.

"The Autonomy of Pantomime." *The Curtain*, IX, No. 106 (Oct., 1930), p. 125.

"Black Butterflies." *Forum*, LI, No. 2 (Feb., 1914), pp. 299-304.

"Chaplin's 'City Lights'." *The Curtain*, X, No. 111 (March, 1931), p. 38.

"A Conversation with Henry Janeway Hardenbergh." *Architectural Record*, XIX (May 24, 1906), pp. 376-80.

"Eastman Johnson." *International Studio*, XXXIV (April, 1908), pp. 106-11.

"Ecclesiastical Sculpture in America." *Catholic World*, No. 12 (Sept., 1903), pp. 760-67.

"The Edgar Saltus I Knew." *Bookman*, LVIII, No. 1 (Sept., 1923), pp. 17-19.

"Eremites of the Brush." *American Mercury*, XI, No. 42 (June, 1927), pp. 192-96.

"An Expression of Decorative Sculpture—Leo Lentelli." *Architect and Engineer of California*. LII (March, 1918), p. 59-68.

"From a Hollywood Studio: Chaplin the Conceited—His luck—And His Genius." *The Curtain*, IV, No. 47 (November, 1925), p. 146.

"The Fourth Day." *Bruno's Review of Two Worlds*, I, No. 3 (Jan., 1921), p. 80.

"In Perfume Land." *Forum*, I, No. 2 (August, 1913), pp. 217-28.

"The Invisible Drama." *The Curtain*, XI, No. 121 (Jan., 1932), p. 3.

"Japanese Drama." *Forum*, XLVII, No. 6 (June, 1912), pp. 724-34.

"Japanese Fiction." *Forum*, XLV, No. 6 (June, 1911), pp. 725-33.

"*Leitmotiv*." Introduction to *Whisperings of a Wind Harp*, by Anne Throop. New York, 1897.

"My Rubaiyat." *Bruno Chap Books*, III, No. 5 (May, 1916).

"Nominations for the 1939 Art Derby New York City (During the Farley Period of Art)." With a biographical statement. 1939.

"Our American Art Museums." *Arts and Decoration*, V (1915) pp. 358-60, 387-89, 419-21, 464-67, 492.

"Permanent Peace: Is It A Dream?" *Bruno Chap Book*, II, No. 4 (Oct., 1915)

————. "Repetition With Slight Variation." *Camera Work*, No. 1 (Jan., 1903), pp. 30-34.

————. "Rodin's Balzac." *Camera Work*, No. 34/35 (April-July, 1911), pp. 19-21.

"Salut Au Monde: A Friend Remembers Whitman." *Southwest Review*, XII, No. 4 (Summer, 1927), pp. 262-67.

"Shooting in Japan." *Outing*, XXI (March, 1893), pp. 427-31.

—————. "That Toulouse Lautrec Print." *Camera Work*, No. 29 (Jan., 1910), pp. 36-38.

"A Visit to John Burroughs." *The Century Magazine*, CI, n.s. LXXIX, No. 5 (March, 1921), pp. 619-21. Reprinted in: Law, Frederick Houk, *Modern Essays and Stories*. New York: The Century Co., 1922, pp. 100-07.

"Where are the Gestures of Yesterday?" *The Curtain*, IX, No. 97 (Jan., 1930), pp. 3-4.

BOOKS AND ARTICLES ABOUT SADAKICHI HARTMANN

Blake, Elizabeth Stanton. "*Un Correspondant Americain De Mallarme, avec deux lettres et un document inedits.*" *Revue d'Histoire Litteraire de la France*, LXVIII (Jan., Feb., 1968), pp. 26-35.

Boswell, Peyton. "Peyton Boswell Comments; King of Bohemia." *Art Digest*, XIX, No. 5 (Dec. 1, 1944), p. 3.

Burke, J. F. *Noah*. New York: Bantam Books, 1969.

Craven, Wayne. *Sculpture in America*. New York: Thomas Y. Crowell Co., 1968, p. 557. One recent book which mentions Hartmann as "an eminent critic and historian of American Art."

Current Opinion. "The Most Mysterious Personality in American Letters." Vol. LXI (Aug., 1916), pp. 124-25.

De Casseres, Benjamin. "Five Portraits on Galvanized Iron." *American Mercury*, IX (Dec., 1926), pp. 397-98.

Dickson, Samuel. "San Francisco is your Home." *Tales of San Francisco*. Stanford, California: Stanford University Press, 1957, pp. 230-238.

Elderman, Michael J. "Sadakichi Hartmann and Stephane Mallarme." *Sadakichi Hartmann Newsletter*, I, No. 1 (Fall, 1969), pp. 3-4.

Fowler, Gene. *Good Night, Sweet Prince*. New York: The Viking Press, 1944, pp. 446-50.

—————. *Minutes of the Last Meeting*. New York: The Viking Press, 1954.

Goldman, Emma. *Living My Life*. New York: Alfred A. Knopf, 1931. See especially, Vol. I, pp. 119, 377.

Hansen, Helga. "Requiem (In Memory of Sadakichi Hartmann)," *Art Digest*, XIX, No. 6 (Dec. 15, 1944), p. 24.

Hill, Richard. "The First Hippie." *Swank International*, XVI, No. 2 (April, 1969), pp. 16-18.

—————. "The Life and Times of Sadakichi Hartmann." *Florida Accent*, (Nov. 10, 1968), pp. 8-10.

Horr, Alexander S. "Sadakichi Hartmann as a Photographic Writer." *Photo-Beacon*, XVI (Oct., 1904), pp. 307-09.

Lawton, Harry. "Book Review: *Edgar Saltus*, by Claire Sprague." *Sadakichi Hartmann Newsletter*, I, No. 1 (Fall, 1969), p. 3.

—————. "The Last Bohemian." *Fortnight*, XIX, No. 4 (April, 1956), p. 31.

Knox, George. "The Beginning of the *Sadakichi Hartmann Newsletter*." *Sadakichi Hartmann Newsletter*, I, No. 1 (Fall, 1969), pp. 1-2.

Paige, D. D., ed. *The Letters of Ezra Pound*. New York: Harcourt, Brace, and World, Inc., 1950, p. 341.

Van Doren, Carl. "A Hero With His Posse." *Roving Critic*. New York: Alfred A. Knopf, 1923, pp. 219-20.

Walsh, Elizabeth Blanche. "On the Natural Drama" (Review of *Tragedy in a New York Flat). Freelance Magazine*, May 1, 1904.

—Compiled by Michael J. Elderman

Bonham: *First Ibsen Performance in Boston*
ca. 1915 (Cat. No. 47)

SADDAMEUY

AUDV

ROUKEODU

HAEVIE 2 DV